GUMBALL GRAMMAR

2¢

nouns·verbs·adjectives·adverbs·pronouns

WRITTEN BY LINDA SCHWARTZ

ILLUSTRATED BY BEVERLY ARMSTRONG

THE LEARNING WORKS

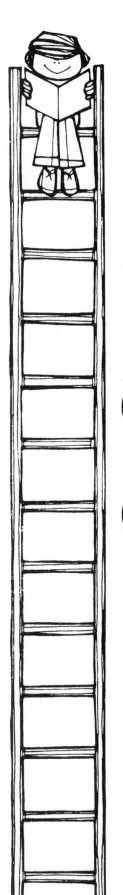

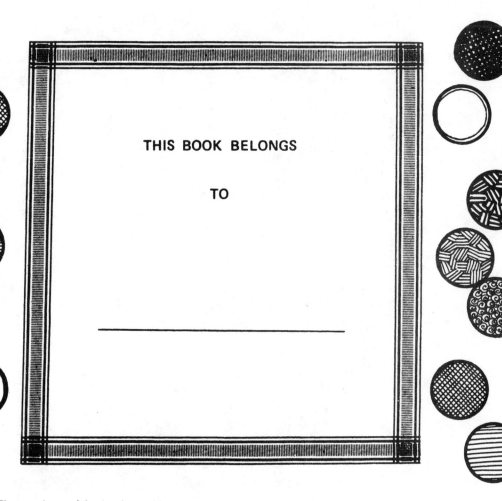

THIS BOOK BELONGS

TO

_____

The purchase of this book entitles the individual
classroom teacher to reproduce copies for use
in the classroom.

The reproduction of any part for an entire school
or school system or for commercial use is strictly
prohibited.

No form of this work may be reproduced or
transmitted or recorded without written permis-
sion from the publisher.

GUMBALL GRAMMAR
TABLE OF CONTENTS

NAME _____

NOUN GUMBALLS

A **common noun** names a person, place, or thing. Examples: city, doctor
A **proper noun** names a **particular** person, place or thing. Examples: Miami, Dr. Jones
(Always capitalize **proper nouns**.)

Find the nouns in the gumball machine.
Write the nouns in the proper places below.

Texas · was · pretty · Bill · gum · Canada · Dr. Davis · Asia · teeth · dog · brother · Kathy · mom · chewy · California · machine · never · Mexico · slowly · Australia · is · candy · also · mouth · bubble · New York · father · sister

2¢

PERSON	PLACE	THING
sister		

NAME _____

PICK-A-NOUN PROVERBS

A proverb is a popular saying.

A. Write a common noun on each line to complete the proverb.

1. An _____ a _____ keeps the _____ away.

2. Too many _____ spoil the _____ .

3. Every _____ has a silver _____ .

4. A rolling _____ gathers no _____ .

5. A _____ and his _____ are soon parted.

6. _____ is the _____ of all _____ .

7. A _____ in the _____ is worth two in the _____ .

8. Don't cry over spilled _____ .

9. Don't count your _____ before they hatch.

10. Don't put all your _____ into one _____ .

<table>
<tr><td colspan="2">CLUE BOX</td></tr>
</table>

CLUE BOX

| bird |
| moss |
| cloud |
| broth |
| stone |
| money |
| day |
| hand |
| fool |
| milk |
| apple |
| bush |
| lining |
| eggs |
| doctor |
| basket |
| root |
| cooks |
| chickens |
| evil |
| money |

B. Find the nouns above in the maze. Answers are found going up,
    down, forward, backward, and diagonally.

C	O	O	K	S	S	O	M	L	B	K	D
B	H	L	A	G	R	O	B	L	I	E	G
R	F	I	P	G	N	A	U	I	R	L	A
O	G	E	C	E	S	V	S	N	D	P	E
T	D	A	Y	K	M	K	H	I	M	P	V
H	Q	U	E	D	E	O	S	N	I	A	I
R	O	T	C	O	D	N	N	G	L	C	L
F	O	O	L	U	N	V	S	E	K	G	B
C	L	O	U	D	A	H	T	S	Y	R	K
Y	Z	R	B	O	H	E	N	O	T	S	R

JUST FOR FUN

1. Pick a proverb above, or choose one of your own.

2. Change each word in the proverb to make it sound more fancy.

3. Use a thesaurus for help.

Example: Refrain from weeping in reaction to a dairy product that has overflowed.

NAME _____

SPECIAL FAVORITES

REMEMBER!

> A proper noun names a particular person, place, or thing.
> Proper nouns always begin with a capital letter.

Write a proper noun for each of your favorites.
Remember to start with a capital letter.

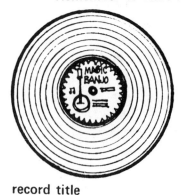

television show

record title

book title

_____

make of car

_____

a particular person I'd like to meet

_____

a particular city I'd like to visit

_____

MORE FAVORITES . . .

holiday _____   sports hero _____

restaurant_____   actor/actress_____

day of the week _____   singer _____

month of the year _____   store _____

tourist attraction _____   teacher _____

movie _____   country I'd like to travel to _____

NAME _____

NIFTY SIXTY NOUN GAME

Write a noun for each category.

Your noun must start with the letter given.

	b	t	g	p	s
animal					
article of clothing					
occupation or profession					
fruit or vegetable					

Use lower case letters for these common nouns.

Possible score

20

Score _____

	c	f	b	r	t
game or sport					
thing to eat					
fish or bird					
things found in a house					

Use lower case letters for these common nouns.

Possible score

20

Score _____

	G	L	M	P	T
city					
famous person (last name) dead or alive					
foreign country					
movie or T.V. show					

Use capital letters for these proper nouns.

Possible score

20

Score _____

NAME _____

GUMBALLS GALORE

> A plural is a word that means more than one. (Examples: coins, girls)
>
> Form most plural nouns by adding s to the singular noun. (Example: bubble-bubbles)
>
> Add es to form the plural noun if the singular noun ends in s, ss, x, ch, or sh.
> (Example: box-boxes)

A. Make the words plural by adding the correct ending.

Write the plural form of the nouns in the gumball machine.

1. ear
2. fox
3. bench
4. doctor
5. circus
6. tax
7. dress
8. splash
9. mix
10. bush

11. ring
12. bunch
13. orange
14. smile
15. lunch
16. witch
17. chair
18. brick
19. push
20. paper

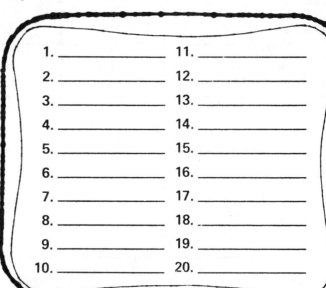

1. _____ 11. _____
2. _____ 12. _____
3. _____ 13. _____
4. _____ 14. _____
5. _____ 15. _____
6. _____ 16. _____
7. _____ 17. _____
8. _____ 18. _____
9. _____ 19. _____
10. _____ 20. _____

B. EXCITING EXCEPTIONS

Write the plural form for each noun.

Since these nouns follow no specific rules when forming plurals, use your dictionary if you need help.

1. mouse _____
2. leaf _____
3. woman _____
4. child _____
5. ox _____
6. tooth _____
7. foot _____
8. goose _____
9. man _____
10. fish _____

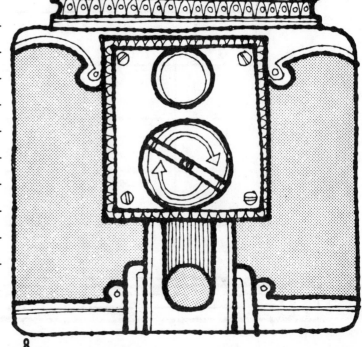

SUPER SPIES

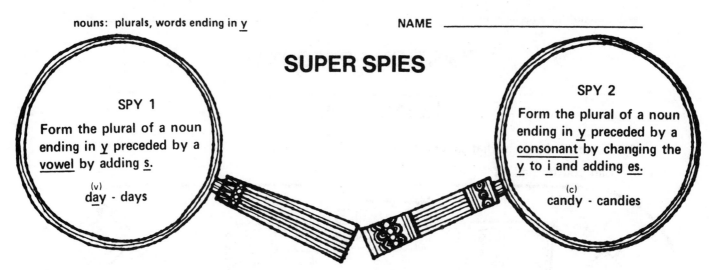

SPY 1

Form the plural of a noun ending in <u>y</u> preceded by a <u>vowel</u> by adding <u>s</u>.

(v)
d<u>a</u>y - days

SPY 2

Form the plural of a noun ending in <u>y</u> preceded by a <u>consonant</u> by changing the <u>y</u> to <u>i</u> and adding <u>es</u>.

(c)
candy - candies

Use the rules above and write the plural form of these nouns in the correct spy.

SPY 1   SPY 2

boy
spy
berry
valley
city
key
toy
penny
lady
pony
turkey
supply
party
play
baby
ray
journey
story
monkey
tray

9

ACTION SPEEDWAY

| A <u>verb</u> can show action. |

A. Circle all the verbs that show action.

Can you find all 28?

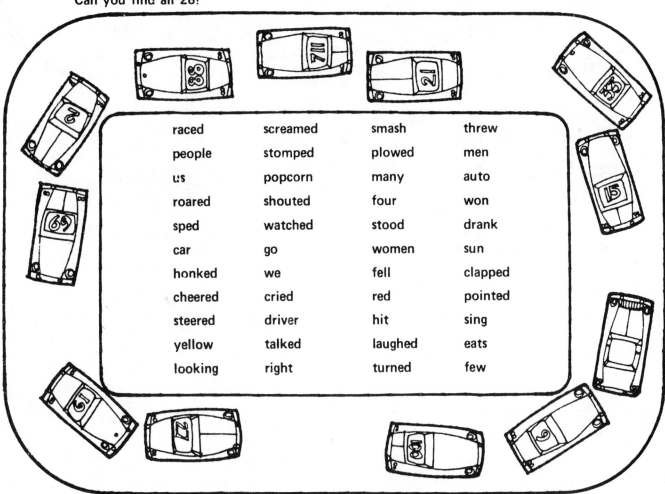

raced	screamed	smash	threw
people	stomped	plowed	men
us	popcorn	many	auto
roared	shouted	four	won
sped	watched	stood	drank
car	go	women	sun
honked	we	fell	clapped
cheered	cried	red	pointed
steered	driver	hit	sing
yellow	talked	laughed	eats
looking	right	turned	few

B.   Underline the two action verbs in each sentence. Write these verbs on the lines.

1. The bikers pedaled hard as they rode up the hill.   _____

2. The country singer played the guitar as he sang.   _____

3. She dove off the high board and swam across the pool.   _____

4. They danced to the disco music and clapped their hands. _____

5. He tossed the ball into the net and scored the winning points. _____

6. The jogger ran across the field and then stopped to rest. _____

7. The team fumbled the ball and lost the game.   _____

8. The tennis player jumped into the air and slammed the ball. _____

NAME _____

HELPING VERB PIZZA

> A helping verb is used to make the form of another verb.

These sentences have a main verb and a helping verb.

The main verbs have been underlined for you.

Circle all the helping verbs.

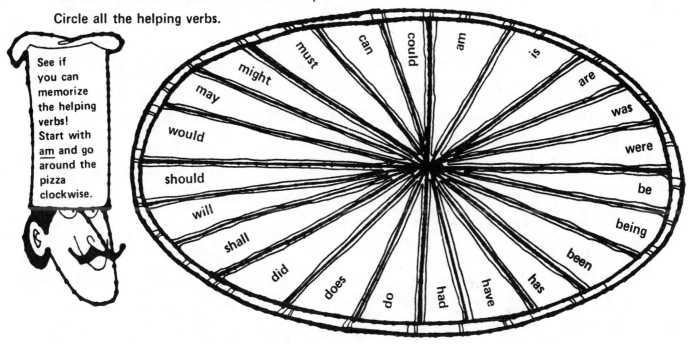

See if you can memorize the helping verbs! Start with am and go around the pizza clockwise.

1. The chef read the announcement: There is going to be a contest to see who can make the best pizza. You may enter the contest if you have been registered as a member of the Pizza Club. Prizes will be given for the most creative pizza.

2. "That does seem interesting," thought the chef. "I do enjoy contests. I must try to win the prize."

3. "I shall try something that has never been attempted before," the chef said to himself.

4. Before he could think of what special ingredients he could add, his friend appeared.

5. "I was passing by and decided I would stop and see if you had heard about the pizza contest. I am planning to enter and hoped you might consider entering too," said his friend.

6. "The contest does sound good. I had planned to enter and have decided what secret topping will be added to my pizza," replied the chef.

Complete the story on a separate piece of paper.

SUPER SLEUTH

| Not all verbs show action. Some verbs express being. |
| Verbs of being: am, is, are, was, and were. |

Find the verb of being in each sentence.

Write it on the line.

1. I am Super Sleuth. _____

2. There is something you should know about me. _____

3. I am the best detective in the world. _____

4. There were many cases I solved that no other detective would handle. _____

5. There is no case too hard for me. _____

6. I was the detective responsible for capturing Leif, the thief. _____

7. Leif was one of the ten most wanted criminals. _____

8. Police are always calling me to help solve difficult cases. _____

9. Right now I am on the trail of "Slippery Fingers" Fremont. _____

10. He is in big trouble. _____

11. Fremont was the person who stole the famous Dixie Diamond. _____

12. His fingerprints were at the scene of the crime. _____

13. He was not very smart because he forgot to wear gloves. _____

14. I am about to capture Fremont. _____

15. There is suspense all around. _____

Write sentences about Super Sleuth and "Slippery Fingers" Fremont.

Use the verb of being that is indicated before each sentence.

(am)   1. _____

(is)   2. _____

(are)   3. _____

(was)   4. _____

(were) 5. _____

NAME _____

VILLAIN IN THE VERBS

One word in each group is __NOT__ a verb.

Help Super Sleuth find the word that is __NOT__ a verb and write it on the line.

1. run   red   kick   did   twist   _____

2. open   am   look   brown   leaped   _____

3. sing   laugh   was   read   early   _____

4. smiled   being   five   do   moved   _____

5. been   slowly   fumble   write   nod   _____

6. have   toss   bounce   us   wished   _____

7. cooked   you   had   slam   were   _____

8. skinny   shall   loved   slept   is   _____

9. would   gobbled   hoped   closet   picked   _____

10. pencils   must   tapped   washed   fed   _____

11. are   wondered   wrote   orange   may   _____

12. meat   meet   shake   hugged   be   _____

ABC VERB CHALLENGE

Can you write an action verb for each letter listed below?

Time yourself: 1-2 minutes - fantastic   2-3 minutes - very good   3-4 minutes - good

          4-5 minutes - fair

A _____   I _____   R _____

B _____   J _____   S _____

C _____   K _____   T _____

D _____   L _____   U _____

E _____   M _____   V _____

F _____   N _____   W _____

G _____   O _____   Y _____

H _____   P _____   Z _____

NAME _____

YUMMY ADJECTIVES

Adjectives describe nouns.

Adjectives answer the questions, "How many?", "What kind?" or "Which one?"

Circle the adjective on each line.

Write the adjective in the correct column.

	HOW MANY?	WHAT KIND?	WHICH ONE?
(these) buns			these
juicy hamburgers			
three pickles			
red catchup			
that flavor			
many calories			
fresh meat			
huge appetite			
bubbly cheese			
few crumbs			
two patties			
crisp lettuce			
those fries			
strong mustard			
one tomato			

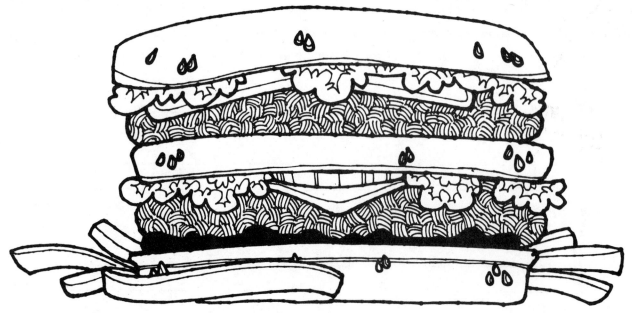

NAME _____

RHYME TIME

Fill in each blank with an adjective that rhymes with the noun.

1. colorless man   **pale**   male
2. droopy flower _____ daisy
3. timid insect _____ fly
4. amusing rabbit _____ bunny
5. glad father _____ pappy
6. fat twig _____ stick
7. lawful dog _____ beagle
8. angry employer _____ boss
9. chubby rodent _____ rat
10. naughty twins _____ trouble
11. noisy mob _____ crowd

CREATE AN AD

Congratulations! You have just been hired to write an advertising slogan for the products below.

1. Give each product a clever name. Decorate the containers.
2. Write a brief description of each product.
3. Include at least <u>five</u> adjectives in your descriptions.

CEREAL

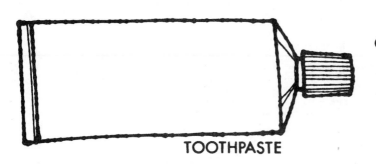

TOOTHPASTE

_____
_____
_____
_____
_____
_____
_____

_____
_____
_____
_____
_____
_____
_____

NAME _____

THE CREEPY CREATURE

Find and underline the adjectives found in the sentences. There are 29 in all.

Make sure the adjectives answer the questions, "How many?", "What kind?", or "Which one?"

A. 1. It was a clear day, so I decided to take a quick walk on the hot, deserted beach.

2. The wet, cool sand felt good on my bare toes.

3. Suddenly I came across two clear footprints in the hardened sand.

4. Each footprint had three claws with sharp, pointed nails.

5. These huge prints were made by an unknown beast!

6. Perhaps it was a green, scaly creature the size of a towering skyscraper.

7. Who would believe this unusual finding?

8. I wanted someone else to see the weird footprints.

9. I spotted an elderly man and brought him to the exact spot.

10. The strange prints had disappeared with the incoming tide.

11. The old man gave me a crazy look and walked away.

B. Imagine that you actually <u>saw</u> the creature on the beach.

Fill in the blanks with adjectives that describe the creature you saw.

_____ eyes (how many)   _____ mouth (what kind)

_____ nose (what kind)   _____ fangs (what kind)

_____ tail (which one)   _____ legs (which ones)

_____ claws (what kind)   _____ body (what kind)

_____ ears (which ones)   _____ weight (what kind)

_____ scales (how many)   _____ teeth (how many)

NAME _____

THE CREEPY CREATURE

Finish the story about the creature.

Use at least ten adjectives in your story.

Underline the adjectives.

_____
_____
_____
_____
_____
_____
_____
_____
_____
_____

Draw a picture of the creature, keeping in mind the adjectives you used.

Noun determiners are words that signal that a noun is coming.

Examples: a, an, the, any, every, each, some, few, many, several, this, that, these, those.

In the newspaper article below, circle the adjectives, including noun determiners, on each line. There are 22 in all.

CREATURE SPOTTED ON BEACH!

A young man described seeing an unbelievable creature today.

He claims he saw this creature in the early morning.

He was the only person to make this wild claim.

Many people think he made the mysterious creature up.

The man insists a huge creature came out of the cold water.

He claims it made deep tracks in the wet sand.

NAME _____

THE BIGGEST BUBBLE

Adjectives can be used to compare nouns.

Add er when comparing two nouns.

Add est when comparing more than two nouns.

Example:

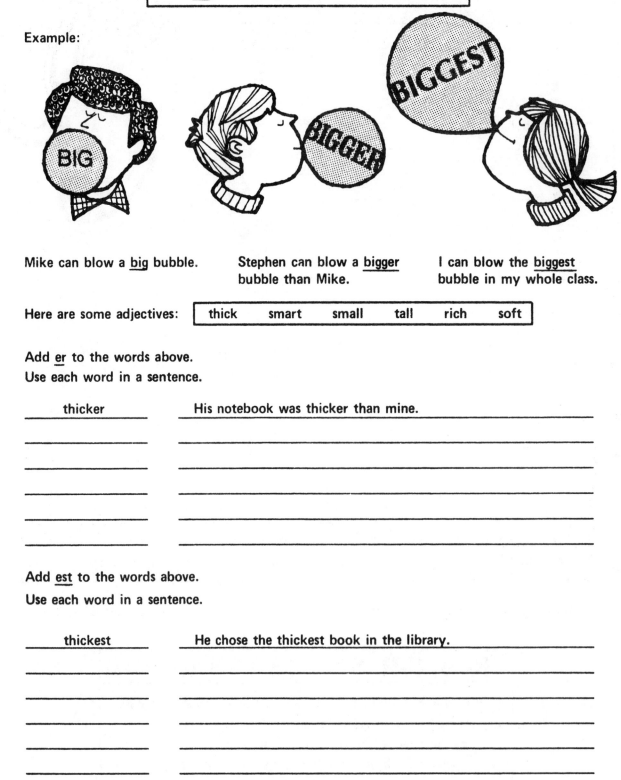

Mike can blow a big bubble.

Stephen can blow a bigger bubble than Mike.

I can blow the biggest bubble in my whole class.

Here are some adjectives:

| thick | smart | small | tall | rich | soft |

Add er to the words above.

Use each word in a sentence.

thicker   His notebook was thicker than mine.

_____   _____

_____   _____

_____   _____

_____   _____

_____   _____

Add est to the words above.

Use each word in a sentence.

thickest   He chose the thickest book in the library.

_____   _____

_____   _____

_____   _____

_____   _____

_____   _____

NAME _____

THE ADVERB COMPUTER

An __adverb__ answers the question "__How__?", "__When__?" or "__Where__?"

Many adverbs end in __ly__ when describing how.

Circle the adverbs on the computer tape.

Write the adverbs in the proper section of the computer.

| far | happily | pencil | below | often | rapidly | dirty | me | near |

| carefully | run | outside | never | cleverly | quickly | sometime | greedily |

| us | soon | here | now | button | slowly | there | ring | seldom |

| yesterday | inside | quietly | above | later |

❋ ADVERB COMPUTER ❋

HOW	WHEN	WHERE

| a | b | c | d | e | f | g | h | i | j | k | l | m |
| n | o | p | q | r | s | t | u | v | w | x | y | z |

NAME _____

WORD TWISTS

Underline the adverb. Write it on the line.

A. 1.   "Don't be chicken," John grumbled foully.   _____

   2.   "This piano is out of tune," the musician stated flatly.   _____

   3.   Kathy said frankly, "These hot dogs are great!"   _____

   4.   "You've got a point there," the teacher said sharply.   _____

   5.   "I've broken my left leg," she said lamely.   _____

   6.   The sheriff said disarmingly, "Drop your gun."   _____

   7.   "Watch that spear!" the native cried pointedly.   _____

   8.   "The building is on fire!" she yelled hotly.   _____

   9.   "This desert is blazing hot," he said dryly.   _____

  10.   "We've struck oil!" the drilling team cried gushingly.   _____

B.   Write a news article for the newspaper about a flying saucer.
     Include an adverb on each line that answers the question in parentheses.

FLYING SAUCER SPOTTED!
(how)
(when)
(where)
(how)
(when)
(where)

NAME _____

WHAT'S THE SCOOP?

Write the correct word on the line.

Circle the <u>noun</u> or <u>verb</u> the word describes.

REMEMBER: An <u>adjective</u> describes a <u>noun</u> and tells how many, what kind, or which one.

An <u>adverb</u> describes a <u>verb</u> and tells how, when, or where.

	ADJECTIVE	ADVERB
1. I felt like buying a _____ ice cream cone.	delicious	deliciously
2. I walked _____ to the nearest ice cream store.	quick	quickly
3. The _____ store was filled with people.	noisy	noisily
4. _____ voices could be heard all over.	loud	loudly
5. First I looked _____ at all the flavors.	careful	carefully
6. It was not an _____ decision to make.	easy	easily
7. I _____ decided and took a number to wait my turn.	final	finally
	slow	slowly
8. The numbers were called so _____ .	quiet	quietly
9. I waited _____ until my number was called.	fantastic	fantastically
10. It was worth waiting for this _____ ice cream cone.		

MAPLE NUT	ENGLISH TOFFEE	CARAMEL NUT	CASHEW
PEPPERMINT	ROCKY ROAD	COCONUT	GRAPE
COFFEE	BUTTER	APPLE PIE	BANANA
BLUEBERRY	CHEES	LICORICE	MANGO
PISTACHIO	RASPB	OOT BEER	DATE NUT
ALMOND FUDGE	POME	LEMON	PECAN PIE
CHERRY PIE	CHOC	IP WBERRY	ORANGE
MINT CHIP	PEANU	TANGERINE	LIME
PINEAPPLE	BUR	RICOT	MOCHA
MARSHMALLOW	C LA	W NUT	VANILLA
EGG NOG	FUDG	ALINE	PEACH
BLACK CHERRY	BOYSE	SPEARMINT	PUMPKIN

21

HAUNTED PRONOUNS

> Pronouns take the place of nouns.
> Singular pronouns: I, he, she, it, you, me
> Plural pronouns: we, you, they, us, them, her, him

Write a pronoun for each underlined noun phrase. Write the pronoun in the haunted house.

A. 1. Dave and Diane approached the haunted house carefully.

2. The vacant house was said to be filled with ghosts and spirits.

3. Dave was about to turn around and go home.

4. Diane insisted they explore inside.

5. The two went inside and saw a winding staircase.

6. The staircase was covered with cobwebs.

7. Diane and Dave slowly began climbing the stairs.

8. A strange and haunting screech came from upstairs.

What do you think made the noise?

_____

_____

Sometimes pronouns can be used as objects in a sentence.
Example: Shall I call him?

B.   Write a sentence and use each object pronoun in the ghost.

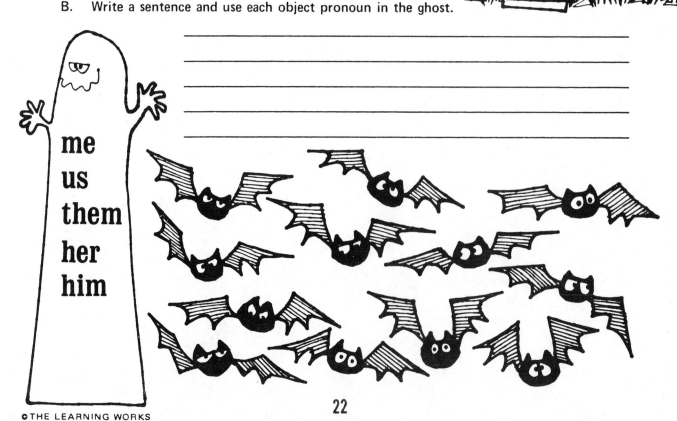

me
us
them
her
him

22

NAME _____

THE PLURAL POSSE

> Some <u>pronouns</u> can show ownership.
> <u>Possessive pronouns:</u> his, her, hers, its, their, theirs, our, ours, your, yours, my, mine

A. Round up the possessive pronouns in each sentence.
Draw a circle around each possessive pronoun.

1. The sheriff told his men to get on their horses.
2. "It is your job to help me capture the bank robbers," he said.
3. "Our task is not going to be easy," said one of the posse.
4. "Their tracks are easy to follow," the sheriff replied.
5. "These wider tracks are hers," exclaimed the sheriff.
6. "Over here you can see where his tracks follow."
7. "If I were you, I would keep my eyes glued to the tracks."
8. "Fame will be ours if we capture them."

> <u>Indefinite pronouns</u> combine two words.

B. Can you combine the words in part A with the words in part B and write 12 indefinite pronouns?

A		B	
any	no	one	
some	every	body	thing

anyone _____   _____
_____   _____
_____   _____
_____   _____
_____   _____
_____   _____

Write four sentences using an indefinite pronoun as
the subject of your sentence.

1. _____

2. _____

3. _____

4. _____

23

THE DREAM?

Underline the pronouns. There are 29 in all.

1. They are out to get us, Dad, take my word!
2. Believe me, they were here just a few minutes ago.
3. I saw the two of them.
4. Their bodies were covered with purple hair.
5. I knew they were not from Earth when I heard one of them make a horrible, growling sound with his voice.
6. The other one glared at me and there was a terrifying look in her eyes.
7. She made a signal and they both left my room.
8. I noticed they were both wearing silver belts around their waists.
9. "You should go back to sleep," said Dad. "You probably had a nightmare."
10. As he walked out, Dad bent down to pick up something he spotted in my rug.
11. He held a silver belt in his hand!

Finish the story.
Use at least six of the pronouns listed above.
Underline the pronouns in your story.

_____
_____
_____
_____
_____
_____
_____
_____
_____

©THE LEARNING WORKS   24

NAME _____

THE WACKY RACE

> A <u>preposition</u> is used to give a noun position.
>
> A <u>prepositional</u> phrase begins with a preposition and ends with a noun.

A. Find and underline the prepositions. Can you find 26?

Hint: ___(behind)___ the crowd. (A preposition will make sense on the line.)

paper	into	by	about
behind	near	in	those
us	below	always	against
around	under	on	tear
with	sky	down	among
above	over	before	fruit
blue	them	cabin	through
beside	inside	six	book
thirty	from	across	within
between	at	toward	rain

B. Underline the prepositional phrase in each sentence.
Write the preposition on the line.

1. <u>Under the grandstands</u>, a restless crowd waited.   **<u>under</u>**

2. Fearless Peerless was just coming into the stadium.   _____

3. He was going to jump his motorcycle over ninety cars.   _____

4. People were cheering and screaming around the stands.   _____

5. Fearless Peerless's cycle had flags streaming behind the seat. _____

6. A rabbit's foot hung from the handlebars for luck.   _____

7. Silver stars were painted on the tires.   _____

8. Under the seat were two jet canisters.   _____

9. Fearless walked toward the crowd.   _____

10. He mounted his cycle and rode across the field.   _____

11. Up the ramp he sailed and began his dangerous jump.   _____

Finish the story. Write two sentences having prepositional phrases.

_____

_____

NAME _____

THE POSSESSIVE PET

Possessives are used to show ownership.

> To show that something belongs to a person or thing, add 's to the word
> if it is a singular word (only one of something). Dad's sandwich was on
> the table.

A.   Write the name of something that belongs to each person or thing.

1. the monster's _____   6. the book's _____

2. a doctor's _____   7. the teacher's _____

3. the rocket's _____   8. an airplane's _____

4. the child's _____   9. the football player's _____

5. the car's _____   10. the dog's _____

B.   Rewrite each group of words to make them show ownership.

1. the report card of Stan _____

2. the dress of the lady _____

3. the tail of the monkey _____

4. the sandwich of the teenager _____

5. the surfboard of Jeff _____

6. the cry of the baby _____

> To show plural ownership of words when the plural ends in s, add only an apostrophe:
> all the dogs' tails. If the plural does not end in s, add 's: men's.

C.   PLURAL POSSESSIVE

Write the name of something that belongs to each person or try to show plural
possession: the drums' sound.

the boys' _____   the babies' _____

the cheerleaders' _____   the animals' _____

the children's _____   the surfers' _____

the women's _____   the bowlers' _____

NAME _____

THE CONTRACTION SKATEBOARD

> A <u>contraction</u> is used to show letters have been left out when combining two words. they have = they've

A. Write a contraction for these words.
Remember the apostrophe.

is not	_____	are not	_____
do not	_____	did not	_____
was not	_____	has not	_____
does not	_____	have not	_____
could not	_____	can not	_____
would not	_____	should not	_____

B. Write a contraction on each blank line.

1. I _____ describe how much fun skateboarding is!
   <u>can not</u>

2. It _____ take long to learn how to ride.
   <u>does not</u>

3. Riding a skateboard_____ difficult once you learn how to balance.
   <u>is not</u>

4. There are a few rules you _____ forget.
   <u>should not</u>

5. _____ ride your skateboard on a crowded sidewalk.
   <u>Do not</u>

6. You _____ ride after dark.
   <u>must not</u>

7. I _____ found any sport I enjoy as much as skateboarding.
   <u>have not</u>

C. Write two words for these contractions.

weren't	_____	you've	_____
hadn't	_____	there's	_____
mustn't	_____	I've	_____
I'd	_____	where's	_____
it's	_____	you're	_____
they'll	_____	she'll	_____

NAME _____

THE MARBERRY MARATHON

Every sentence has a <u>subject</u> and a <u>predicate</u>.
<u>Subject</u>: tells what the sentence is about   The Marberry Marathon
<u>Predicate</u>: tells about the subject   is a famous event.

A.   Draw a box around the subject to separate it from the predicate in each sentence.

1. The joggers were ready for the Marberry Marathon to begin.

2. They had warmed up and were anxious to start.

3. Men, women, and children were participating in the race.

4. It was a perfect day for a race.

5. A warm sun and a gentle breeze could be felt.

6. Most of the joggers wore shorts and tee shirts.

7. Each runner had to wear a number for identification.

8. Noisy crowds lined the street to watch.

9. Photographers and reporters were on hand to cover the event.

10. Excitement and tension were in the air.

11. The announcer told everyone to line up.

12. The Marberry Marathon was about to begin.

B.   Pretend you are a jogger in the Marberry Marathon. Write a predicate to complete each sentence. Separate the subject and predicate in each of your sentences as you did above.

A large crowd _____

The hot sun _____

All the other joggers _____

The cheering crowds _____

Some of the photographers _____

Two young boys _____

My poor feet _____

I _____

NAME _____

WHO ARE YOU?

Circle <u>all</u> the adjectives that describe YOU.

creative	truthful	sincere	graceful
happy	strong	healthy	prompt
athletic	sensitive	gentle	sloppy
lonely	grumpy	dainty	courteous
smart	kind	agreeable	active
brave	scientific	stingy	curious
serious	outgoing	glamorous	moody
shy	excitable	artistic	helpful
quick	humorous	lazy	musical
restless	lucky	dependable	popular

A DIAMOND POEM

Follow this pattern to create your own diamond poem:

line 1: a noun or pronoun

line 2: two adjectives describing the word on line 1

line 3: three action verbs

line 4: an adjective, noun, verb, and adverb (any order)

line 5: a prepositional phrase of three words

line 6: an adjective and a noun

line 7: an adjective

EXAMPLE:

<u>Me</u>

<u>happy, creative</u>

<u>thinking, questioning, eating</u>

<u>gabby person talking always</u>

<u>on the telephone</u>

<u>athletic girl</u>

<u>smart</u>

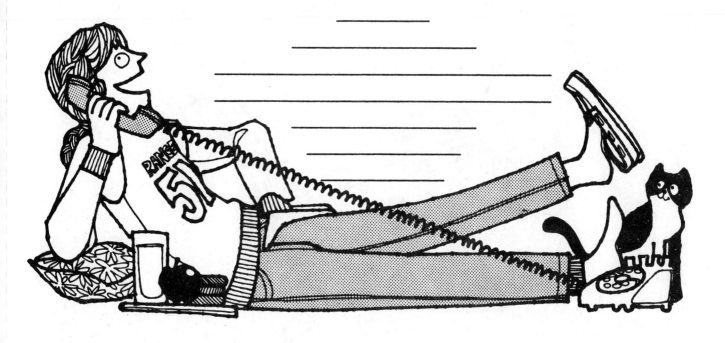

NAME _____

GUMBALL REVIEW

Decide what part of speech each underlined word is and find the letter for it in the box. For each sentence, there is a numbered blank below. Write the letters in the blanks to solve the riddle.

N	V	adj	adv	pron
Ⓘ	B	D	E	A
U	S	C	A	K
O	E	A	I	L
I	C	D	A	G
J	O	B	D	S
T	K	C	B	I
K	L	H	R	T
Y	U	P	Q	V
Y	T	W	X	R
M	D	L	V	N
E	A	T	C	D
S	E	O	R	H
M	F	H	O	I
A	I	B	S	M
T	N	P	D	A

1. A <u>girl</u> walked up to the gumball machine.
2. She saw <u>many</u> gumballs filled to the top.
3. She <u>searched</u> in her purse and found two coins.
4. She <u>carefully</u> dropped the coins in the slot.
5. The girl turned the knob <u>slowly</u>.
6. <u>She</u> waited patiently, but nothing happened.
7. No gumball fell into her <u>outstretched</u> hand.
8. She shook the <u>machine</u> several times.
9. The gumballs <u>moved</u> inside, but none came out.
10. She tapped the machine with <u>her</u> fist. Nothing happened.
11. She was starting to get mad at the <u>stubborn</u> machine.
12. <u>Finally</u> she gave it a swift kick.
13. All seventy-nine gumballs came pouring <u>out</u>!
14. The gumballs <u>made</u> a huge heap on the floor.
15. The girl <u>took</u> one and walked away.

Where can you always find bubble gum?

<u>I</u> __ __ __ __ __ __ __ __ __ __ __ __ __ __
1 15 11 7 3   5 14 2 9 6 13 10 4 12 8

30

 # ANSWERS

PAGE 4   NOUN GUMBALLS: Person - mom, Kathy, sister, Dr. Davis, brother, father, Bill. Place - California, Asia, Mexico, Texas, New York, Canada, Australia. Thing - gum, bubble, candy, dog, mouth, machine, teeth

PAGE 5   PICK-A-NOUN PROVERBS: A. 1. apple, day, doctor   2. cooks, broth   3. cloud, lining   4. stone, moss   5. fool, money   6. money, root, evil   7. bird, hand, bush   8. milk   9. chickens   10. eggs, basket
B.

PAGE 8   GUMBALLS GALORE - A. 1. ears   2. foxes   3. benches   4. doctors   5. circuses   6. taxes   7. dresses   8. splashes   9. mixes   10. bushes   11. rings   12. bunches   13. oranges   14. smiles   15. lunches   16. witches   17. chairs   18. bricks   19. pushes   20. papers   B. 1. mice   2. leaves   3. women   4. children   5. oxen   6. teeth   7. feet   8. geese   9. men   10. fish

PAGE 9   SUPER SPIES: Spy 1 - boys, valleys, keys, toys, turkeys, plays, rays, journeys, monkeys, trays
Spy 2 - spies, berries, cities, pennies, ladies, ponies, supplies, parties, babies, stories

PAGE 10   ACTION SPEEDWAY: A. raced, roared, sped, honked, cheered, steered, looking, screamed, stomped, shouted, watched, go, cried, talked, smash, plowed, stood, fell, hit, laughed, turned, threw, won, drank, clapped, pointed, sing, eats.   B. 1. peddled, rode   2. played, sang   3. dove, swam   4. danced, clapped   5. tossed, scored   6. ran, stopped   7. fumbled, lost   8. jumped, slammed

PAGE 11   HELPING VERB PIZZA: 1. is, can, may, have been, will be.   2. does, do, must   3. shall, has been   4. could, could   5. was, would, had, am, might   6. does, had, have, will be

PAGE 12   SUPER SLEUTH: 1. am   2. is   3. am   4. were   5. is   6. was   7. was   8. are   9. am   10. is   11. was   12. were   13. was   14. am   15. is

PAGE 13   VILLAIN IN THE VERBS: 1. red   2. brown   3. early   4. five   5. slowly   6. us   7. you   8. skinny   9. closet   10. pencils   11. orange   12. meat

PAGE 14   YUMMY ADJECTIVES: **how many** - three, many, few, two, one   **what kind** - juicy, red, fresh, huge, bubbly, crisp, strong   **which one** - these, that, those

PAGE 15   RHYME TIME: 1. pale   2. lazy   3. shy   4. funny   5. happy   6. thick   7. legal   8. cross   9. fat   10. double   11. loud

PAGE 16   THE CREEPY CREATURE: A. 1. clear, quick, hot, deserted   2. wet, cool, bare   3. two, clear, hardened   4. each, three, sharp, pointed   5. these, huge, unknown   6. green, scaly, towering   7. this unusual   8. weird   9. elderly, exact   10. strange, incoming   11. old, crazy   B. answers will vary

PAGE 17   THE CREEPY CREATURE: A young, an unbelievable, this, the early, the only, this wild, many, the mysterious, The, a huge, the cold, deep, the wet.

PAGE 18   THE BIGGEST BUBBLE: thicker, smarter, smaller, taller, richer, softer, thickest, smartest, smallest, tallest, richest, softest. Sentences will vary.

PAGE 19   THE ADVERB COMPUTER: **how** - happily, rapidly, carefully, cleverly, quickly, greedily, slowly, quietly   **when** - often, never, sometime, soon, now, yesterday, later, seldom   **where** - far, below, near, outside, here, there, inside, above

PAGE 20   WORD TWISTS: A. 1. foully   2. flatly   3. frankly   4. sharply   5. lamely   6. disarmingly   7. pointedly   8. hotly   9. dryly   10. gushingly   B. sentences will vary

PAGE 21   WHAT'S THE SCOOP?: 1. delicious - cone   2. quickly - walked   3. noisy - store   4. loud - voices   5. carefully - looked   6. easy - decision   7. finally - decided   8. slowly - called   9. quietly - waited   10. fantastic - cone

PAGE 22   HAUNTED PRONOUNS: A. 1. They   2. It   3. He   4. She   5. They   6. It   7. They   8. It
B. Sentences will vary.

PAGE 23   THE PLURAL POSSE: A. 1. his, their   2. your   3. Our   4. Their   5. hers   6. his   7. my   8. ours

B. anyone   someone   no one   everyone
    anybody   somebody   nobody   everybody
    anything   something   nothing   everything

PAGE 24   THE DREAM?: 1. They, us, my   2. me, they   3. I, them   4. Their   5. I, they, I, them, his
6. me, her   7. She, they, my   8. I, they, their   9. You, You   10. he, something, he, my   11. He, his

PAGE 25   THE WACKY RACE: A. behind, around, with, above, beside, between, into, near, below, under, over, inside,
from, at, by, in, on, down, before, across, toward, about, against, among, through, within

B. 1. <u>Under the grandstands</u> - under   2. <u>into the stadium</u> - into   3. <u>over ninety cars</u> - over
4. <u>around the stands</u> - around   5. <u>behind the seat</u> - behind   6. <u>from the handlebars</u> - from
7. <u>on the tires</u> - on   8. <u>Under the seat</u> - Under   9. <u>toward the crowd</u> - toward   10. <u>across the field</u> - across
11. <u>Up the ramp</u> - Up

PAGE 26   THE POSSESSIVE PET: A. answers will vary   B. 1. Stan's report card   2. the lady's dress
3. the monkey's tail   4. the teenager's sandwich   5. Jeff's surfboard   6. the baby's cry   C. answers will vary

PAGE 27   THE CONTRACTION SKATEBOARD: A. isn't, don't, wasn't, doesn't, couldn't, wouldn't, aren't, didn't,
hasn't, haven't, can't, shouldn't   B. 1. can't   2. doesn't   3. isn't   4. shouldn't   5. Don't   6. musn't   7. haven't

C. were not   you have
    had not   there is
    must not   I have
    I would or
      I had   where is
    it is   you are
    they will   she will

PAGE 28   THE MARBERRY MARATHON: A. 1. The joggers   2. They   3. Men, women, and children   4. It
5. A warm sun and a gentle breeze   6. Most of the joggers   7. Each runner   8. Noisy crowds   9. Photographers and
reporters   10. Excitement and tension   11. The announcer   12. The Marberry Marathon   B. sentences will vary

PAGE 30   GUMBALL REVIEW: parts of speech: noun, adjective, verb, adverb, adverb, pronoun, adjective, noun, verb, pronoun,
adjective, adverb, adverb, verb, verb   Riddle: IN THE DICTIONARY

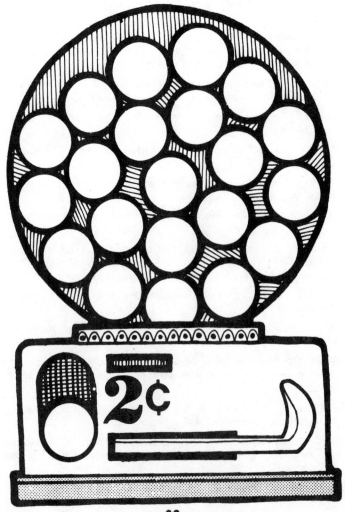